AURORA PRESENTS DON BLUTH PRODUCTIONS'

The Secret of NIMH

W9-CEA-686

DEEP IN A DARK AND MYSTERIOUS CHAMBER, THE LATEST ENTRY IN A JOURNAL IS BEING MADE...

Jonathan Brisby was killed today while helping with the plan. It is four years since our departure, and our world is changing... we cannot stay here much longer.

Jonathan was such a dear friend. I don't know how to help his widow...she knows nothing of us or the plan~~ Best, perhaps, that I do nothing at present. *Nicodemus*

AND SO, MRS. BRISBY FOLLOWS THE DEFEATED DRAGON INTO THE WATER...

SPLOSH!

WHERE SHE RIDES THE WATERWHEEL UP AND INTO THE MILL...

OH, BOO-HOO-HOO-HOO!

HEY, MISS MOUSE! DON'T WORRY! I'M OKAY! BOY, THE WAY I DEALT WITH THAT CAT!

THAT'S NOT THE REASON I'M CRYING, JEREMY!

I LOST TIMMY'S MEDICINE!

TCH-TCH! SORRY!

OH, BOO-HOO-HOO!

THE GREAT OWL, FEARSOME TO BEHOLD, OFFERS STRANGE ADVICE AFTER HEARING OF MRS. BRISBY'S PLIGHT...

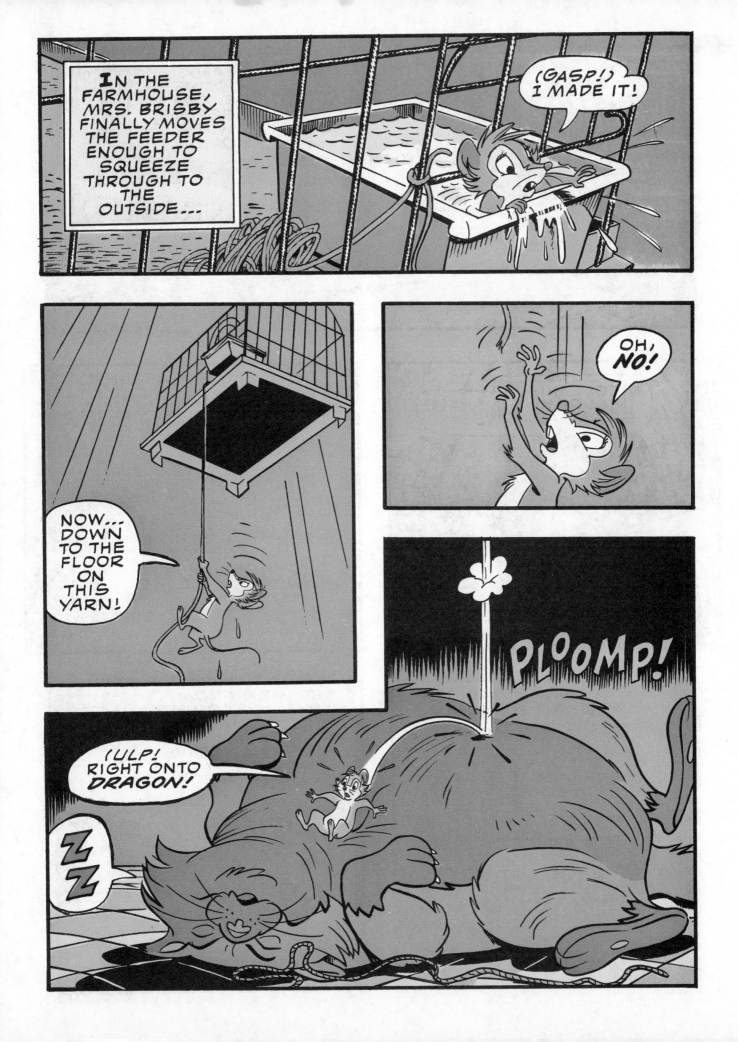